PLAY JAZZ!

Hits from the 20s and 30s

for flute and piano
arranged by Roy Stratford and Sally Adams

Charleston *Mack & Johnson*   page 2

Someone to watch over me *Gershwin*   page 4

Swanee *Gershwin & Caesar*   page 7

I'm getting sentimental over you *Bassman & Washington*   page 10

Do it again *Gershwin & De Sylva*   page 12

Pennies from heaven *Johnston & Burke*   page 14

He loves and she loves *Gershwin*   page 16

I got rhythm *Gershwin*   page 18

© 2002 by Faber Music Ltd
First published in 2002 by Faber Music Ltd
3 Queen Square London WC1N 3AU
Cover design by S & M Tucker
Cover illustration by Lynette Williamson
Music processed by New Notations
Printed in England by Caligraving Ltd
All rights reserved

ISBN 0-571-51822-2

To buy Faber Music publications or to find out about the full range of titles available
please contact your local music retailer or Faber Music sales enquiries:

Faber Music Ltd, Burnt Mill, Elizabeth Way, Harlow CM20 2HX England
Tel: +44 (0)1279 82 89 82   Fax: +44 (0)1279 82 89 83
sales@fabermusic.com   fabermusic.com

CHARLESTON

Music and original lyrics
by Cecil Mack and James Johnson

Quick and lively

* ⌐ ¬ = optional

SOMEONE TO WATCH OVER ME

(*Oh Kay!* 1926)

Music and original lyrics
by George and Ira Gershwin

SWANEE

(Broadway Brevities 1920)

Music and original lyrics
by George Gershwin and Irving Caesar

I'M GETTING SENTIMENTAL OVER YOU

Music and original lyrics
by Bassmann and Washington

Relaxed and free

molto rall.

DO IT AGAIN

Music and original lyrics
by George Gershwin and B.G. De Sylva

PENNIES FROM HEAVEN

Music and original lyrics
by Arthur Johnston and John Burke

HE LOVES AND SHE LOVES

(Funny Face 1927)

Music and original lyrics
by George and Ira Gershwin

Optional ending (from bar 34):

I GOT RHYTHM

(*Girl Crazy*)

Music and original lyrics
by George and Ira Gershwin

Fast and light